LIFE ON THE FARM

PRISCILLA

BOOK 1

First Edition

PAGE PUBLISHING, INC.
New York, NY

First originally published by Page Publishing, Inc. 2018

ISBN 978-1-64027-453-2 (Hardcover)
ISBN 978-1-64027-454-9 (Digital)

Printed in the United States of America

LIFE ON THE FARM
BOOK 1
PRISCILLA
Judy A. Hoff

Mom came home with a strange box. It had lots of holes in it and made funny sounds. I ran over as she lifted the lid. Inside were fluffy baby chicks. Mom smiled and said we should take them to the coop. As we walked, the chicks made their funny chirping sounds.

"Why are they so noisy?' I asked.

"You will see," she replied.

Once inside the coop, I realized Mom had been very busy. It was clean. There were warm lights hanging and many feeders and waterer on the floor. We carefully took each chick from the box and dipped their beaks in the water, giving each their first drink. We then put them under the warm lights. Mom was counting as she did this.

She said "Oh" as she lifted one very small chick last from the box. "This one does not look good."

As I held the small chick, the rest began to run every which way—under the lights, to the food, to the water, and back again.

"They were hungry," I said.

Soon I would have to put the little chick down. I did so by laying it under a light after giving it a drink.

I ran to the coop the next morning to find them all running around. I filled their feeders and also the waterer, all the time looking for the small chick. There she was under one of the lights. I picked her up and named her Priscilla.

As they grew, they lost their fluffy and got real feathers. The days of summer were warm, and they were let out during the day to chase bugs and eat grass. The chicks grew fast. Keeping them fed was a big job, but Mom said I could do it. Priscilla grew but not as big as the rest. Whenever she saw me, she would come running. I would hold her as I did the rest of my chores.

Soon all the young hens started sitting in the nests and happily began laying small brown eggs. I never saw Priscilla even near the nest and was worried Mom might notice.

One day I came home, and there was no Priscilla to be seen anywhere. Where could she be? Did she get lost or hurt? Days went by and still no Priscilla.

I was worried I would never see her again. Then twenty-one days after she went missing, I saw her sitting near the tall grass.

She saw me but did not come running to me. As I slowly walked to her, I heard her making soft clucking sounds. I picked her up.

Surprise! She had a pile of fuzzy chicks under her.

I ran to get Mom. We picked her and the chicks up. We made a nice place for them in a shed where they would be safe. I counted the chicks as I put them down, six of them. I noticed one of them was bigger, and it was darker.

I looked at Mom and said, "I think I will name this one Alex."

About the Author

Judy A Hoff lives in Southwestern North Dakota with her husband Mark. Together they run a cattle ranch. Growing up on a ranch and raising two kids there also, she has many stories to tell.